*TASK CARD SERIES*

Conceived and
written by
**Ron Marson**
Illustrated by
**Peg Marson**

LEARNING
SYSTEMS

10970 S. Mulino Rd.
Canby OR 97013

*Dear Educator,*
*Please excuse our transition . . .*

TOPS open-ended task card modules are taking on a new look. Task cards that used to come printed 4-up on heavy index card stock, packaged 2 sets to a zip-lock bag, are now printed 2-up at the back of this single book.

Even though our new cards are printed on lighter book stock, even though we haven't included an extra copy, we can now offer you something much better: You have our permission to make as many photocopies of these task cards as you like, as long as you restrict their use to the students you personally teach. This means you now can (1) incorporate task cards into full-sized worksheets, copying the card at the top of the paper and reserving the bottom for student responses. (2) You can copy and collate task card reference booklets, as many as you need for student use. Or (3) you can make laminated copies to display in your classroom, as before.

It will take some time to fully complete this transition. In the interim we will be shipping TOPS modules as a mixture of both old and new formats. Effective immediately (September 1989) this newer, more liberal photocopy permission applies to all task cards, including our older, heavier, 4-up standards!

*Happy sciencing,*

*Ron Marson*
*author/publisher*

ISBN 0-941008-74-6

Printed on Recycled Paper ♻

# CONTENTS

## INTRODUCTION

## TEACHING NOTES

## REPRODUCIBLE STUDENT TASK CARDS

# A TOPS Model for Effective Science Teaching...

***If science were only a set of explanations*** and a collection of facts, you could teach it with blackboard and chalk. You could assign students to read chapters and answer the questions that followed. Good students would take notes, read the text, turn in assignments, then give you all this information back again on a final exam. Science is traditionally taught in this manner. Everybody learns the same body of information at the same time. Class togetherness is preserved.

***But science is more than this.***

Science is also process — a dynamic interaction of rational inquiry and creative play. Scientists probe, poke, handle, observe, question, think up theories, test ideas, jump to conclusions, make mistakes, revise, synthesize, communicate, disagree and discover. Students can understand science as process only if they are free to think

and act like scientists, in a classroom that recognizes and honors individual differences.

Science is *both* a traditional body of knowledge *and* an individualized process of creative inquiry. Science as process cannot ignore tradition. We stand on the shoulders of those who have gone before. If each generation reinvents the wheel, there is no time to discover the stars. Nor can traditional science continue to evolve and redefine itself without process. Science without this cutting edge of discovery is a static, dead thing.

Here is a teaching model that combines the best of both elements into one integrated whole. It is only a model. Like any scientific theory, it must give way over time to new and better ideas. We challenge you to incorporate this TOPS model into your own teaching practice. Change it and make it better so it works for you.

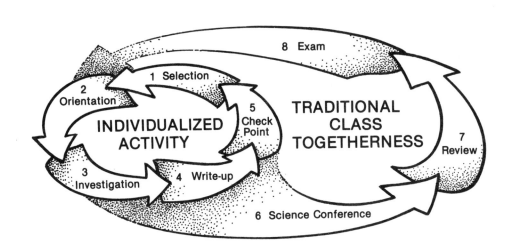

## 1. SELECTION

Doing TOPS is as easy as selecting the first task card and doing what it says, then the second, then the third, and so on. Working at their own pace, students fall into a natural routine that creates stability and order. They still have questions and problems, to be sure, but students know where they are and where they need to go.

Students generally select task cards in sequence because new concepts build on old ones in a specific order. There are, however, exceptions to this rule: students might *skip* a task that is not challenging; *repeat* a task with doubtful results; *add* a task of their own design to answer original "what would happen if" questions.

## 2. ORIENTATION

Many students will simply read a task card and immediately understand what to do. Others will require further verbal interpretation. Identify poor readers in your class. When they ask, "What does this mean?" they may be asking in reality, "Will you please read this card aloud?"

With such a diverse range of talent among students, how can you individualize activity and still hope to finish this module as a cohesive group? It's easy. By the time your most advanced students have completed all the task cards, including the enrichment series at the end, your slower students have at least completed the basic core curriculum. This core provides the common background so necessary for meaningful discussion, review and testing on a class basis.

# 3. INVESTIGATION

Students work through the task cards independently and cooperatively. They follow their own experimental strategies and help each other. You encourage this behavior by helping students only *after* they have tried to help themselves. As a resource person, you work to stay *out* of the center of attention, answering student questions rather than posing teacher questions.

When you need to speak to everyone at once, it is appropriate to interrupt individual task card activity and address the whole class, rather than repeat yourself over and over again. If you plan ahead, you'll find that most interruptions can fit into brief introductory remarks at the beginning of each new period.

# 4. WRITE-UP

Task cards ask students to explain the "how and why" of things. Write-ups are brief and to the point. Students may accelerate their pace through the task cards by writing these reports out of class.

Students may work alone or in cooperative lab groups. But each one must prepare an original write-up. These must be brought to the teacher for approval as soon as they are completed. Avoid dealing with too many write-ups near the end of the module, by enforcing this simple rule: each write-up must be approved *before* continuing on to the next task card.

# 5. CHECK POINT

The student and teacher evaluate each write-up together on a pass/no-pass basis. (Thus no time is wasted haggling over grades.) If the student has made reasonable effort consistent with individual ability, the write-up is checked off on a progress chart and included in the student's personal assignment folder or notebook kept on file in class.

Because the student is present when you evaluate, feedback is immediate and effective. A few seconds of this direct student-teacher interaction is surely more effective than 5 minutes worth of margin notes that students may or may not heed. Remember, you don't have to point out every error. Zero in on particulars. If reasonable effort has not been made, direct students to make specific improvements, and see you again for a follow-up check point.

A responsible lab assistant can double the amount of individual attention each student receives. If he or she is mature and respected by your students, have the assistant check the even-numbered write-ups while you check the odd ones. This will balance the work load and insure that all students receive equal treatment.

# 6. SCIENCE CONFERENCE

After individualized task card activity has ended, this is a time for students to come together, to discuss experimental results, to debate and draw conclusions. Slower students learn about the enrichment activities of faster students. Those who did original investigations, or made unusual discoveries, share this information with their peers, just like scientists at a real conference. This conference is open to films, newspaper articles and community speakers. It is a perfect time to consider the technological and social implications of the topic you are studying.

# 7. READ AND REVIEW

Does your school have an adopted science textbook? Do parts of your science syllabus still need to be covered? Now is the time to integrate other traditional science resources into your overall program. Your students already share a common background of hands-on lab work. With this shared base of experience, they can now read the text with greater understanding, think and problem-solve more successfully, communicate more effectively.

You might spend just a day on this step or an entire week. Finish with a review of key concepts in preparation for the final exam. Test questions in this module provide an excellent basis for discussion and study.

# 8. EXAM

Use any combination of the review/test questions, plus questions of your own, to determine how well students have mastered the concepts they've been learning. Those who finish your exam early might begin work on the first activity in the next new TOPS module.

Now that your class has completed a major TOPS learning cycle, it's time to start fresh with a brand new topic. Those who messed up and got behind don't need to stay there. Everyone begins the new topic on an equal footing. This frequent change of pace encourages your students to work hard, to enjoy what they learn, and thereby grow in scientific literacy.

# GETTING READY

Here is a checklist of things to think about and preparations to make before your first lesson.

## ☐ Decide if this TOPS module is the best one to teach next.

TOPS modules are flexible. They can generally be scheduled in any order to meet your own class needs. Some lessons within certain modules, however, do require basic math skills or a knowledge of fundamental laboratory techniques. Review the task cards in this module now if you are not yet familiar with them. Decide whether you should teach any of these other TOPS modules first: *Measuring Length, Graphing, Metric Measure, Weighing* or *Electricity* (before *Magnetism*). It may be that your students already possess these requisite skills or that you can compensate with extra class discussion or special assistance.

## ☐ Number your task card masters in pencil.

The small number printed in the lower right corner of each task card shows its position within the overall series. If this ordering fits your schedule, copy each number into the blank parentheses directly above it at the top of the card. Be sure to use pencil rather than ink. You may decide to revise, upgrade or rearrange these task cards next time you teach this module. To do this, write your own better ideas on blank 4 x 6 index cards, and renumber them into the task card sequence wherever they fit best. In this manner, your curriculum will adapt and grow as you do.

## ☐ Copy your task card masters.

You have our permission to reproduce these task cards, for as long as you teach, with only 1 restriction: please limit the distribution of copies you make to the students you personally teach. Encourage other teachers who want to use this module to purchase their *own* copy. This supports TOPS financially, enabling us to continue publishing new TOPS modules for you. For a full list of task card options please turn to the first task card masters numbered "cards 1-2."

## ☐ Collect needed materials.

Please see the opposite page.

## ☐ Organize a way to track completed assignment.

Keep write-ups on file in class. If you lack a vertical file, a box with a brick will serve. File folders or notebooks both make suitable assignment organizers. Students will feel a sense of accomplishment as they see their file folders grow heavy, or their notebooks fill up, with completed assignments. Easy reference and convenient review are assured, since all papers remain in one place.

Ask students to staple a sheet of numbered graph paper to the inside front cover of their file folder or notebook. Use this paper to track each student's progress through the module. Simply initial the corresponding task card number as students turn in each assignment.

## ☐ Review safety procedures.

Most TOPS experiments are safe even for small children. Certain lessons, however, require heat from a candle flame or Bunsen burner. Others require students to handle sharp objects like scissors, straight pins and razor blades. These task cards should not be attempted by immature students unless they are closely supervised. You might choose instead to turn these experiments into teacher demonstrations.

Unusual hazards are noted in the teaching notes and task cards where appropriate. But the curriculum cannot anticipate irresponsible behavior or negligence. It is ultimately the teacher's responsibility to see that common sense safety rules are followed at all times. Begin with these basic safety rules:

1. Eye Protection: Wear safety goggles when heating liquids or solids to high temperatures.
2. Poisons: Never taste anything unless told to do so.
3. Fire: Keep loose hair or clothing away from flames. Point test tubes which are heating away from your face and your neighbor's.
4. Glass Tubing: Don't force through stoppers. (The teacher should fit glass tubes to stoppers in advance, using a lubricant.)
5. Gas: Light the match first, before turning on the gas.

## ☐ Communicate your grading expectations.

Whatever your philosophy of grading, your students need to understand the standards you expect and how they will be assessed. Here is a grading scheme that counts individual effort, attitude and overall achievement. We think these 3 components deserve equal weight:

1. Pace (effort): Tally the number of check points you have initialed on the graph paper attached to each student's file folder or science notebook. Low ability students should be able to keep pace with gifted students, since write-ups are evaluated relative to individual performance standards. Students with absences or those who tend to work at a slow pace may (or may not) choose to overcome this disadvantage by assigning themselves more homework out of class.

2. Participation (attitude): This is a subjective grade assigned to reflect each student's attitude and class behavior. Active participators who work to capacity receive high marks. Inactive onlookers, who waste time in class and copy the results of others, receive low marks.

3. Exam (achievement): Task cards point toward generalizations that provide a base for hypothesizing and predicting. A final test over the entire module determines whether students understand relevant theory and can apply it in a predictive way.

# Gathering Materials

Listed below is everything you'll need to teach this module. You already have many of these items. The rest are available from your supermarket, drugstore and hardware store. Laboratory supplies may be ordered through a science supply catalog.

Keep this classification key in mind as you review what's needed:

| *special in-a-box materials:* | general on-the-shelf materials: |
|---|---|
| Italic type suggests that these materials are unusual. Keep these specialty items in a separate box. After you finish teaching this module, label the box for storage and put it away, ready to use again the next time you teach this module. | Normal type suggests that these materials are common. Keep these basics on shelves or in drawers that are readily accessible to your students. The next TOPS module you teach will likely utilize many of these same materials. |
| (substituted materials): | *optional materials: |
| Parentheses enclosing any item suggests a ready substitute. These alternatives may work just as well as the original, perhaps better. Don't be afraid to improvise, to make do with what you have. | An asterisk sets these items apart. They are nice to have, but you can easily live without them. They are probably not worth an extra trip to the store, unless you are gathering other materials as well. |

Everything is listed in order of first use. Start gathering at the top of this list and work down. Ask students to bring recycled items from home. The teaching notes may occasionally suggest additional student activity under the heading "Extensions." Materials for these optional experiments are listed neither here nor in the teaching notes. Read the extension itself to find out what new materials, if any, are required.

Needed quantities depend on how many students you have, how you organize them into activity groups, and how you teach. Decide which of these 3 estimates best applies to you, then adjust quantities up or down as necessary:

$Q_1 / Q_2 / Q_3$

**Single Student:** Enough for 1 student to do all the experiments.
**Individualized Approach:** Enough for 30 students informally working in 10 lab groups, all self-paced.
**Traditional Approach:** Enough for 30 students, organized into 10 lab groups, all doing the same lesson.

| KEY: | *special in-a-box materials* (substituted materials) | general on-the-shelf materials *optional materials |
|---|---|---|

| $Q_1 / Q_2 / Q_3$ | |
|---|---|
| 3/25/30 | index cards - 4x6 inch |
| 1/10/10 | meter sticks |
| 2/10/20 | straight pins |
| 3/30/30 | medium-sized cans — both ends should be removed for activity 5 |
| 8/80/80 | pennies — see notes 7 and 9 |
| 1/5/5 | rolls masking tape |
| 1/3/3 | spools thread |
| 1/10/10 | scissors |
| 1/3/3 | boxes paper clips |
| 1/10/10 | full sheets newspaper |
| 2/20/20 | size-D batteries, dead or alive — see note 13 |
| 3/12/30 | clothespins — wooden are best |
| 1/4/10 | plastic drinking straws |
| 6/60/60 | rubber bands — half thick and half thin |
| 1/10/10 | medium-sized nails — see note 7 |
| 1/10/10 | each of assorted coins: pennies, nickles, dimes, quarters |
| 1/3/3 | rolls clear tape |
| 1/1/1 | roll waxed paper |
| 1/3/10 | small graduated cylinders — 10 ml capacity |
| 1/10/10 | hand calculators |
| 1/1/1 | *wooden see-saw, constructed with saw, hammer and nails - see note 15* |
| 1/1/1 | *bathroom scales |
| 2/6/20 | large plastic milk cartons with handles and lids |
| 2/6/20 | *feet of cord or thin rope* |

# Sequencing Task Cards

This logic tree shows how all the task cards in this module tie together. In general, students begin at the trunk of the tree and work up through the related branches. As the diagram suggests, the way to upper level activities leads up from lower level activities.

At the teacher's discretion, certain activities can be omitted or sequences changed to meet specific class needs. The only activities that must be completed in sequence are indicated by leaves that open *vertically* into the ones above them. In these cases the lower activity is a prerequisite to the upper.

When possible, students should complete the task cards in the same sequence as numbered. If time is short, however, or certain students need to catch up, you can use the logic tree to identify concept-related *horizontal* activities. Some of these might be omitted since they serve only to reinforce learned concepts rather than introduce new ones.

On the other hand, if students complete all the activities at a certain horizontal concept level, then experience difficulty at the next higher level, you might go back down the logic tree to have students repeat specific key activities for greater reinforcement.

For whatever reason, when you wish to make sequence changes, you'll find this logic tree a valuable reference. Parentheses in the upper right corner of each task card allow you total flexibility. They are left blank so you can pencil in sequence numbers of your own choosing.

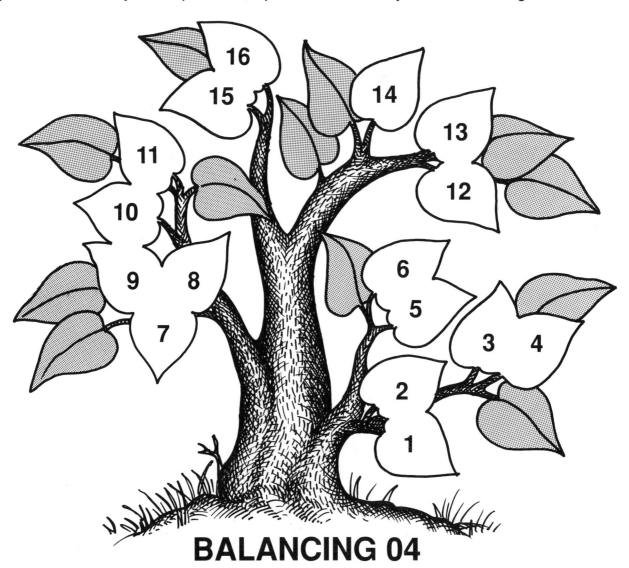

# BALANCING 04

E

# LONG-RANGE OBJECTIVES

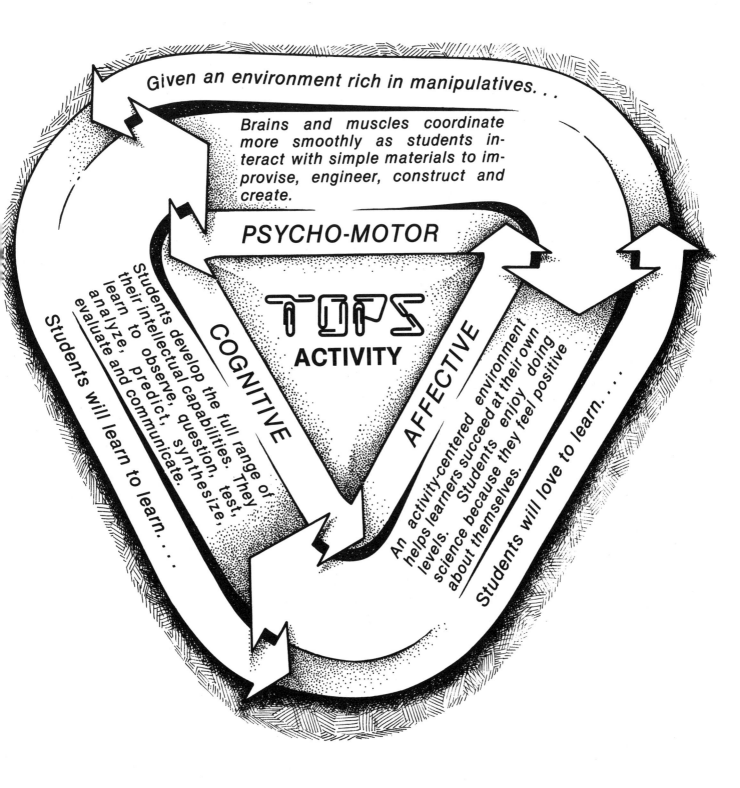

Given an environment rich in manipulatives...

Brains and muscles coordinate more smoothly as students interact with simple materials to improvise, engineer, construct and create.

PSYCHO-MOTOR

TOPS ACTIVITY

COGNITIVE

Students develop the full range of their intellectual capabilities. They learn to observe, question, test, analyze, predict, synthesize, evaluate and communicate.

Students will learn to learn....

AFFECTIVE

An activity-centered environment helps learners succeed at their own levels. Students enjoy doing science because they feel positive about themselves.

Students will love to learn....

# Review / Test Questions

Photocopy the questions below. On a separate sheet of blank paper, cut and paste those boxes you want to use as test questions. Include questions of your own design, as well. Crowd all these questions onto a single page for students to answer on another paper, or leave space for student responses after each question, as you wish. Duplicate a class set and your custom-made test is ready to use. Use leftover questions as a review in preparation for the final exam.

### task 1
Mechanics balance car tires by fixing lead weights, as necessary, to the wheel rims. Explain how this affects the CG of a tire and the car's ride.

### task 1, 5, 6
Imagine balancing an upside-down paper plate on one finger.

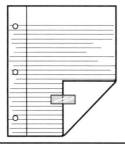

a. Where is the CG in relation to your finger?
b. Why is it easier to balance this plate with the rim down than with the rim up?

### task 2 A
The corner of a sheet of notebook paper is folded and taped like this. Explain how to use a plumb line to find its CG.

### task 2 B
A piece of notebook paper hangs from the tip of a pencil at its corner margin hole. Where is its CG in relation to the pencil point? Explain.

### task 3-4 A
A wine glass rests on a slanting book. What happens to it when you gently fill it with water? Illustrate your answer with a labeled drawing.

### task 3-4 B
Maria is standing on both feet. Can she stand on 1 foot *without* moving her upper body? Explain.

### task 3, 14
How far off the edge of a table can you slide a book before it falls? Illustrate your answer with a drawing.

### task 5-6 A
Is a meter stick more stable resting flat on the table, or standing on end? Use a labeled diagram to illustrate your answer.

### task 5-6 B
Name a 3-dimensional shape that *always* has neutral equilibrium on a level surface.

### task 7
How would you use a centered meter stick balance to determine whether 3 pennies are heavier than 4 dimes?

### task 7-9 A
Here is one way to balance 3 coins against 1 coin on a centered balance. Draw two more ways to balance 3 against 1.

### task 7-9 B
Use math to predict whether each beam will balance. If not, which way will the beam tip?

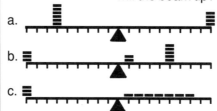

### task 7-9, 13
A bar balances on a centered beam opposite 5 coins of equal mass. What is the mass of the bar in terms of these coins? Explain your reasoning.

### task 10, 11
An eyedropper dispenses 20 drops of water per milliliter. One ml of water equals one gram.
a. What is the mass of 1 drop of water?
b. Exactly 46 drops of water counterbalance 1 dime when placed on opposite sides of a centered balance, equidistant from the pivot. What is the mass of the dime?
c. Exactly 23 drops of water are placed 20 cm from the pivot. How far from the pivot would you place the dime on the opposite side?

### task 10-11, 15-16
A washer balances at the 10 cm position on a centered meter stick opposite 3.0 ml of water at the 90 cm position.
a. What is the mass of the washer?
b. If this washer is placed at the 45 cm position, it balances a paper clip at the 80 cm position. Calculate the mass of the paper clip.

### task 11, 15, 16
A 150 pound adult and a 90 pound child sit on opposite sides of a see-saw. If the adult sits 6 feet from the pivot, where does the child balance?

### task 8-9, 11-12
Heavy weights of equal mass hang from beams of negligible mass. Use math to show why each beam balances.

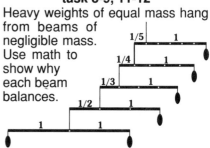

### task 8-9, 11-12
Heavy weights of equal mass hang from beams of negligible mass. Use math to show why each beam balances.

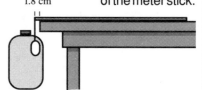

### task 13, 16
A gallon of water (3.78 liters) hung at the end of a meter stick just begins to tip when it hangs 1.8 cm beyond the edge of the table. Calculate the mass of the meter stick.

### task 14
How far beyond a table edge can you cantilever 2 bricks? Draw a labelled diagram as your answer.

# Answers

## task 1
The lead weights shift each tire's CG more toward the center of the tire (directly over the axle), resulting in more smoothly turning wheels and a smoother ride.

## task 1, 5, 6
a. The CG is inside your finger, slightly below the point of contact.

b. Inverting the plate lowers its CG below your fingertip. This increases its stability:
tipping it any way *raises* its CG.

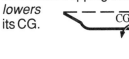

If the plate is rim up, however, it is less stable: tipping it in any direction *lowers* its CG.

## task 2 A
Poke the paper with a pin (or use existing holes) and hang a plumb line on it. The CG of the paper will be located directly behind the thread of the plumb line as both hang freely. Mark this line, and repeat the operation along another plumb line. The CG is located where all lines cross.

## task 2 B
The paper's CG lies directly below the pencil point. Suspend a plumb line from this pencil point, and it will cross the CG.

## task 3-4 A
The glass will eventually tip over. As you fill it with water, the CG rises up the glass until it moves beyond its supporting base.

## task 3-4 B
No. Maria's CG is centered between her feet. If she lifts one foot, she must shift her upper body over the other foot so her CG remains over its single base of support.

## task 3, 14
You can slide a book *almost* halfway off the table. Its CG must remain inside the table edge.

## task 5-6 A
The ruler is more stable resting flat on the table than on end. Resting flat, you have to lift its CG much higher before it becomes unstable and falls in a new direction. Resting on end, you need to tip the ruler very little before its CG begins to fall.

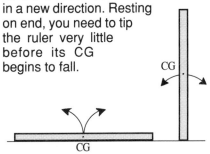

## task 5-6 B
A ball always has neutral equilibrium. Roll it in any direction and the CG moves along the horizontal, neither rising nor falling.

## task 7
Place a stack of 3 pennies opposite a stack of 4 dimes, equidistant from the pivot. The meter stick tips toward the heavier stack of coins.

### task 7-9 A

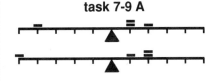

### task 7-9 B
a. $6 \times 6 = 4 \times 9$
$36 = 36$
*balances*

b. $3 \times 9 = 2 + 5 \times 5$
$27 = 27$
*balances*

c. $3 \times 9 = 1 + 2 + 3 + 4 + 5 + 6 + 7$
$27 < 28$
*balance tilts right*

## task 7-9, 13
The bar's center of gravity rests over position 5 on the left:
$$(\text{mass})(\text{dist})_{\text{left}} = (\text{mass})(\text{dist})_{\text{right}}$$
bar mass $\times 5 = 5$ coins $\times 4$
bar mass $= 5$ coins $\times 4/5 = 4$ coins

## task 10, 11
a. 1.0 ml water = 1.0 gram = 20 drops;
1 drop = 1.0 gram / 20 = 0.05 grams

b. 46 drops = (20 + 20 + 6) drops
= 1.0 g + 1.0 g + 6(0.05 g)
= 2.30 grams

c. Place the dime 10 cm from the pivot opposite the water. Because it has twice the mass of the water, it will counterbalance at half the distance.

## task 10-11, 15-16
a. Because the washer and the water balance equidistant from the pivot, they have the same mass:
mass of washer = 3.0 ml water = 3.0 g

b. $(\text{mass})(\text{dist})_{\text{left}} = (\text{mass})(\text{dist})_{\text{right}}$
3.0 g $\times$ 5 cm = clip mass $\times$ 30 cm
clip mass = 3.0 g $\times$ 5/30 = 0.5 g

## task 11, 15, 16
$$(\text{weight})(\text{dist})_{\text{left}} = (\text{weight})(\text{dist})_{\text{right}}$$
150 lb $\times$ 6 ft = 90 lb $\times$ child's dist
child's dist = 6 feet $\times$ 150/90 = 10 ft

## task 8-9, 11-12
$$(\text{mass})(\text{dist})_{\text{left}} = (\text{mass})(\text{dist})_{\text{right}}$$
$5 \times 1/5 = 1 \times 1$
$4 \times 1/4 = 1 \times 1$
$3 \times 1/3 = 1 \times 1$
$2 \times 1/2 = 1 \times 1$
$1 \times 1 = 1 \times 1$

## task 8-9, 11-12
$$(\text{mass})(\text{dist})_{\text{left}} = (\text{mass})(\text{dist})_{\text{right}} + (\text{mass})(\text{dist})_{\text{right}}$$
$9 = 4 + 5$
$7 = 3 + 4$
$5 = 2 + 3$
$3 = 1 + 2$
$1 = 1$

## task 13, 16
Think of the meter stick as a small equal arm balance measuring 1.8 cm on a side. A gallon of water with a mass of 3780 grams bears down on the left. The remainder of the meter stick (96.6 cm) bears down on the right at its CG, 50 cm from the pivot.

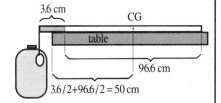

$$(\text{mass})(\text{dist})_{\text{left}} = (\text{mass})(\text{dist})_{\text{right}}$$
3,780 g $\times$ 1.8 cm = mass $\times$ 50 cm
mass = 3780 $\times$ 1.8/50 = 136 g

This load is 96.6 cm long. The entire 100 cm length is a little heavier:
136 g $\times$ 100/96.6 = 141 g

## task 14

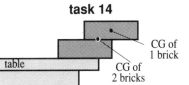

# TEACHING NOTES
## For Activities 1-16

**Task Objective (TO)** find the center of gravity of an index card. To understand why it shifts as mass is added to the card.

---

### CENTER OF GRAVITY  ○                    Balancing (   )

1. On an index card, draw diagonal lines that touch each corner. Use a can to give the card a curve, keeping its diagonals to the inside.

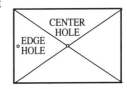

2. Lightly rest your card on a pinpoint where the diagonals cross. Rotate it *horizontally*.

   a. This balance point is called the *center of gravity* (CG). Where is the CG on your index card?

   b. Poke two pinholes through this card: one at its CG, the other near any edge away from the corners. Compare how the card spins *vertically* around a pin through each hole.

3. Tape a penny to a corner of your card. Spin the card on a pin point to locate its new CG, then make a pinhole at this point.

   a. Label this new CG. Compare spinning motions around this point with the other two holes.

   b. Is the CG still centered in the middle of the card? In the middle of its total mass? Explain.

(Write your name on the card and save it.)

*FIND THE NEW CG.*

© 1993 by TOPS Learning Systems                    1

---

### Answers / Notes

2. *The pinpoint supports the spinning card; it must not poke through. If the card slides off, it is too flat. Increase its downward curve by pressing it again (diagonals to the inside) around the side of the can.*

2a. The center of gravity (CG) on the index card is located where the diagonals cross, in the center of the card.

2b. The card rotates smoothly and evenly around its CG, but with variable speed around the outside hole. *(The card also comes to rest at no preferred orientation when the pin is at the CG. It always stops with the CG directly below the pin when spun around the outside hole.)*

3. *To find the new CG students should test various points on the card until they find its unique balance point.*

a. The card spins smoothly and evenly only around this new CG, while spinning at variable speed around the other 2 holes. *(As before, the new CG comes to rest directly below the pin when the other holes are used.)*

b. The CG is no longer located in the middle of the card. It still is, however, located in the middle of its total mass, comprised of the card and penny and tape.

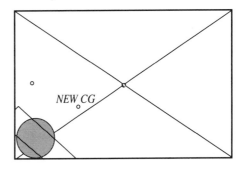

*NEW CG*

### Materials

☐ A 4x6 index card.
☐ A ruler or other straightedge. Folded scratch paper is suitable.
☐ A sharp straight pin.
☐ A medium-sized can.
☐ A penny.
☐ Masking tape.

---

**(TO)** use a plumb line to experimentally determine the CG of an irregular shape.

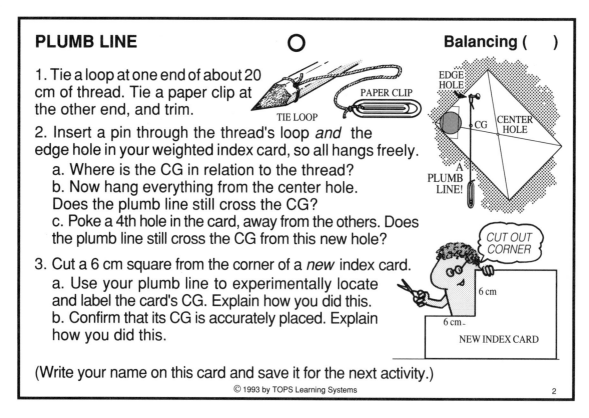

**PLUMB LINE** O **Balancing ( )**

1. Tie a loop at one end of about 20 cm of thread. Tie a paper clip at the other end, and trim.

   PAPER CLIP

   TIE LOOP

2. Insert a pin through the thread's loop *and* the edge hole in your weighted index card, so all hangs freely.
   a. Where is the CG in relation to the thread?
   b. Now hang everything from the center hole. Does the plumb line still cross the CG?
   c. Poke a 4th hole in the card, away from the others. Does the plumb line still cross the CG from this new hole?

   EDGE HOLE
   CG
   CENTER HOLE
   A PLUMB LINE!

3. Cut a 6 cm square from the corner of a *new* index card.
   a. Use your plumb line to experimentally locate and label the card's CG. Explain how you did this.
   b. Confirm that its CG is accurately placed. Explain how you did this.

   CUT OUT CORNER
   6 cm
   6 cm
   NEW INDEX CARD

(Write your name on this card and save it for the next activity.)

2

## Answers / Notes

1. *A thread loop is easy to tie around a solid object, such as a pencil.*

2a. The CG is located right behind the thread, on the vertical plumb line.

2b. Yes. The plumb line hangs over the CG.

2c. Yes.

3a. Hang the card and plumb line from two or more widely separated holes located near the edge of the card. At each hole, mark the resting position of the plumb line with a straight line. Where these lines cross defines the CG.

3b. Students should see whether the card (curved slightly, as before) balances on the pin at this experimental CG point, and/or verify that it spins smoothly and evenly around this point. *(Experimental error in locating the plumb line may show up with these additional tests. Students may repoke the CG hole as necessary.)*

## Materials

☐ Thread.
☐ A meter stick.
☐ Scissors.
☐ A paper clip.
☐ The index card and penny from the previous activity.
☐ A straight pin.
☐ Another 4x6 index card.
☐ A medium-sized can.

**(TO)** observe that an object remains stable as long as its CG remains over its supporting base.

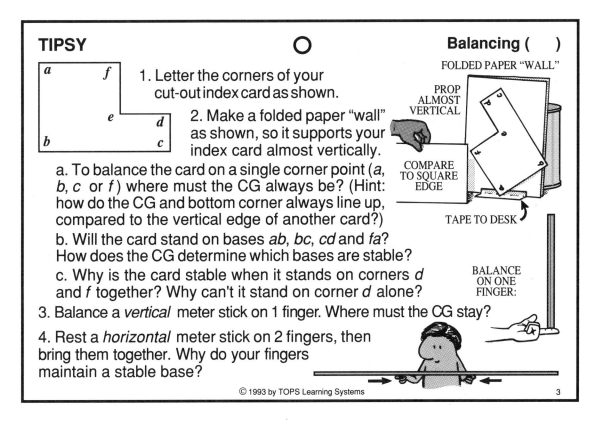

**TIPSY** ○ **Balancing ( )**

1. Letter the corners of your cut-out index card as shown.

2. Make a folded paper "wall" as shown, so it supports your index card almost vertically.

a. To balance the card on a single corner point (*a*, *b*, *c* or *f*) where must the CG always be? (Hint: how do the CG and bottom corner always line up, compared to the vertical edge of another card?)

b. Will the card stand on bases *ab*, *bc*, *cd* and *fa*? How does the CG determine which bases are stable?

c. Why is the card stable when it stands on corners *d* and *f* together? Why can't it stand on corner *d* alone?

3. Balance a *vertical* meter stick on 1 finger. Where must the CG stay?

4. Rest a *horizontal* meter stick on 2 fingers, then bring them together. Why do your fingers maintain a stable base?

© 1993 by TOPS Learning Systems

3

## Answers / Notes

2a. The card balances whenever its CG rests directly above each point of contact. At this position both points line up with the vertical edge of an index card.

2b. The card stands on bases *ab*, *bc* and *fa* because its CG remains *above* each base of support. It won't stand on base *cd* however, because its CG remains outside this base of support.

2c. Corners *d* and *f* form a stable base because a vertical line from the card's CG remains between these support points. The card won't stand on corner *d* alone because you can't position the CG directly above it when this corner touches the table.

3. You must continuously move your finger in order to maintain the meter stick's CG directly above its base point.

4. The fingers maintain a stable base because the meter stick's CG (at the 50 cm mark) always remains between both supporting fingers. *(The ruler rests most heavily on the finger that is nearest to its CG. The farthest finger, with less friction, is the one that always slides closer. This alternating motion maintains a roughly centered CG.)*

## Materials

☐ The index card with the cut-out corner.
☐ Tape.
☐ A sheet of scratch paper.
☐ A can.
☐ An index card.
☐ A meter stick.

**(TO)** feel your body lose stability as your CG shifts relative to your feet.

## AGAINST THE WALL    ○    Balancing (   )

1. When you stand tall, arms at your side, your CG typically rests inside your body, several centimeters below your navel.

*A TYPICAL HUMAN CG . . .*

a. How might you raise your CG closer to your navel?

b. How might you move your CG outside your body?

2. Find some floor space next to a wall and try each challenge. Include a body drawing with each answer similar to this one.

a. Keep both *heels* against the wall. Can you bend over and touch the floor? Why?

b. Keep one *shoulder and foot* against the wall. Can you hold your outside foot off the floor? Why?

c. Keep your *toes and nose* pressed to the wall. Can you raise your heels to stand on your toes? Why?

CG

BASE

4

## Answers / Notes

1a. Raise your hands over your head.

1b. Bend over and touch your toes.

2a. No. As you bend over, your CG moves beyond your feet. You fall forward.

2b. No. When you raise your outside foot, the wall restrains you from shifting your body over your inside foot. Because your CG now lies outside this narrow support base, you fall away from the wall.

2c. No. Shifting your weight from both feet to just your toes moves your base of support out from under your CG. You become unstable and fall backward.

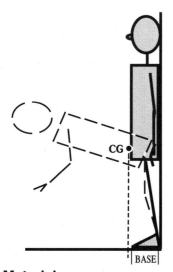

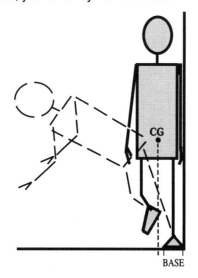

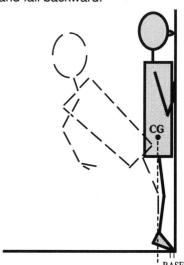

## Materials

☐  Free floor space next to a wall.

**(TO)** define stable, unstable, and neutral equilibrium positions in terms of the displacement in an object's CG.

---

## STABLE / UNSTABLE / NEUTRAL  ◯  Balancing (   )

1. Get 2 cans with both ends removed. Use a wad of newspaper to wedge a size-D battery inside one of them. Mark the CG of each system as shown:

Draw an "x" on tape. The CG is located inside the battery behind this x.

Tape 2 threads across the end of a can to form an "x." The CG is in the center of the can behind this x.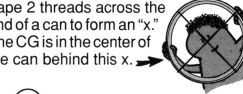

2. Roll both cans across the floor.
   a. Describe how they move and stop.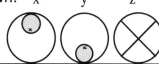
   b. Sketch how the CG moves in each rolling can relative to the floor.

3. Balance the cans in each position **x**, **y** and **z** as shown:
   a. Which position is stable? Unstable? Neutral?
   b. When you move the can at each position, does its CG rise or fall?

   x    y    z

4. The *equilibrium* of a balanced object describes its stability.
   a. Draw a battery in 3 equilibrium positions — stable, unstable and neutral.
   b. When you push it off each equilibrium, how does its CG shift?

© 1993 by TOPS Learning Systems                                    5

---

## Answers / Notes

**2a.** With each revolution, the can with the battery rolls faster, then slower; faster, then slower. It always comes to rest with the battery at the bottom of the can. The empty can, by contrast, rolls smoothly and evenly with no preferred stopping position.

**2b.**  Path of the CG in the can with the battery:

Path of the CG in the empty can:

**3a.** Position **y** is stable. *(Pushing it forward or back raises the CG. Take your finger away and the CG returns to its original position.)*

Position **x** is unstable. *(The slightest disturbance lowers the CG, sending the battery to the bottom of the can.)*

Position **z** is neutral. *(Pushing it neither raises nor lowers the CG. One position is as stable as another.)*

**3b.** Moving the can raises its CG.

Moving the can lowers its CG.

Moving the can neither raises nor lowers its CG.

**4.**

| STABLE EQUILIBRIUM | UNSTABLE EQUILIBRIUM | NEUTRAL EQUILIBRIUM |
|---|---|---|

 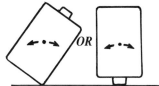 

The CG moves upward.

The CG moves downward.

The CG moves horizontally.

### Materials
- ☐ Two medium-sized cans with both ends removed.
- ☐ A full sheet of newspaper.
- ☐ A size-D battery, dead or alive.
- ☐ Thread.
- ☐ Scissors.
- ☐ Masking tape.

**(TO)** observe how lowering the CG of an object below its pivot point stabilizes its equilibrium.

---

# DANCING ON A PINHEAD  Balancing (   )

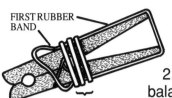

FIRST RUBBER BAND

SECOND RUBBER BAND

1. Hold a thin rubber band over the open end of a clothespin. Secure it with another rubber band near the spring.

2. Clamp the clothespin on the rim of a can, then try to balance a straw on the rubber band. Is its equilibrium stable in this position? Use a drawing to explain why.

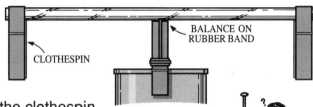

BALANCE ON RUBBER BAND

CLOTHESPIN

3. Hang a clothespin on each end of the straw. How does this affect its equilibrium? Use a drawing to explain your observations.

4. Take both rubber bands off the clothespin. Use them to strap a clothespin "wing" to the side of the can.
   a. Clamp a pin, head up, in the clothespin.
   b. Try this challenge: fix as many paper clips as you like to a *second* pin, so it "toe-dances" on the head of the first!
   c. Sketch your design. Explain why it has stable equilibrium.

© 1993 by TOPS Learning Systems                                                    6

---

## Answers / Notes

2. The straw's equilibrium is unstable. It is very difficult to find a balance point where the straw remains on top of the rubber band. This is because any tipping of the straw *lowers* its CG. (*A precarious balance is possible if the bridging rubber band contains no twists.*)

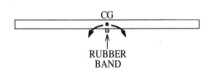

CG

RUBBER BAND

3. When clothespins are hung on each side, the straw's equilibrium becomes stable. Its CG is now located below the pivot, so that any tipping *raises* this point.

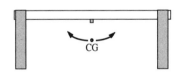

CG

4b. *The challenge here is to attach enough paper clips to the pin to lower its CG well below its pivot point.*

4c. Here is one of many possible designs. The pin is stable because any tipping motion raises its CG.

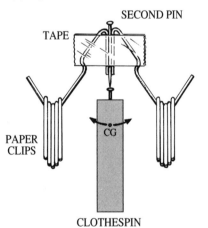

SECOND PIN

TAPE

PAPER CLIPS

CG

CLOTHESPIN

---

## Materials

☐ Three clothespins.
☐ A straw.
☐ A medium-sized can.
☐ Two narrow rubber bands.
☐ Two pins.
☐ Masking tape.
☐ Paper clips.

**(TO)** construct an equal-arm balance beam. To use it to compare the relative masses of different coins.

## METER STICK BALANCE     O             Balancing (   )

1. Rubber-band a nail directly over the 50 cm mark of a meter stick. Wind the rubber band *tightly* over both ends of the nail.

2. Rest the meter stick (nail side up) between 2 cans. Tape a paper clip somewhere underneath so the beam rests level.

RUBBER BAND

BOTTOM DETAIL:

RUBBER BAND

PAPER CLIP RIDER TO LEVEL

3. The beam now balances with the nail on top. Will it also balance with the nail underneath? Why?

4. Use your balance to compare the masses of different coins. If possible include a U.S. penny minted before 1982, and another minted after 1982.

    a. Order the coins from lightest to heaviest. Explain how you did this.

    b. Write your initials on the masking tape that holds the paper clip to your meter stick. Save it to use in activities that follow.

7

## Answers / Notes

1. *Check that students have centered their nails* precisely *over the 50 cm mark, so the millimeter marks emerge equidistant from under both sides of the nail. If the nail is not held firmly in place, add another rubber band. While not so important now, small deviations off this center mark can significantly affect experimental results in later activities.*

2. *If the meter stick is not uniform, several paper clips, or perhaps a coin, may be required to shift its CG directly under the 50 cm mark.*

3. No. The meter stick tips right or left and remains off balance because the CG remains above rather than below the nail. Any motion lowers its CG.

4a. *Here is an ordering for U.S. coins:*

(*least mass* ⟵⟶ *most mass*)

dime, post-1982 penny, pre-1982 penny, nickel, quarter

    To compare coin masses, place them equidistant from the pivot, say at the 10 cm and 90 cm positions. The balance tilts down on the side with the heavier coin.

## Materials

☐ A meter stick.

☐ A medium-sized nail, about 6 cm (2.5 inches) long. Bigger (thicker) nails reduce the balance's sensitivity.

☐ A rubber band. Use a thick one or several thin ones.

☐ Available coins. We recommend using a pre-1982 U.S. penny, post-1982 U.S. penny, nickel, dime and quarter.

☐ Two medium-sized cans.

☐ Paper clips.

☐ Masking tape.

**(TO)** write mathematical equations that express a state of balance on a centered beam.

---

## MATH IN THE BALANCE (1)  ○                 Balancing (    )

1. Balance your meter stick between cans as before. Set a battery under each end so the beam can't tilt too far.

2. Get 3 coins of equal mass. Balance them on the beam at the 10 cm positions shown in 2a:

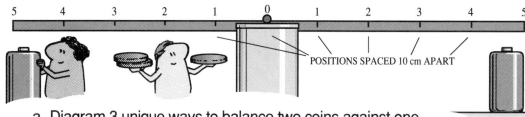

POSITIONS SPACED 10 cm APART

a. Diagram 3 unique ways to balance two coins against one.

b. When does the beam balance? Develop a rule.

3. Get 6 coins of equal mass.
   a. Diagram how the beam looks expressing this equation: $2x2 + 5 = 3x3$.
   b. Invent 3 more interesting equations that use all 6 coins.
   c. Restate your rule for a balanced beam in terms of the *number* of coins at each position and their *distance* from the pivot.

© 1993 by TOPS Learning Systems                                                                8

---

## Answers / Notes

1. *The beam need not balance perfectly level at this point. More refined adjustments will be made in later activities.*

2a.

2b. The beam balances when the sum of the pivot distances for both coins on one side equals the pivot distance for the coin on the other side.

3a.  5  4  3  2  1  /0\  1  2  3  4  5

3b. *Here are 3 more equations among many possibilities. Where numbers are multiplied, the first represents the number of coins, the second is the distance from the pivot.*

$$5 + 3 + 1 = 3x3$$
$$2x5 = 3x2 + 4$$
$$2x4 = 4x2$$

3c. Multiply the number of coins at each position on the balance beam by their distance from the pivot. If the beam balances, then the sum of the products on the left side equals the sum of the products on the right side.

## Extension

• Begin with a pile of 4 coins at 30 cm and 70 cm on a balanced beam. Write an equation.
• Move equal numbers of coins *symmetrically* (in equal and opposite directions). Write an equation.
• Make another symmetry move and write another equation. (Moving across the pivot is OK.)
• Continue making symmetry moves until you generate 10 equations.

## Materials

☐ The meter stick balance plus supporting cans from the previous activity.
☐ Six post-1982 pennies or other coins of equal mass. Check all dates! Just one older, heavier penny complicates the mathematics.
☐ Two size-D batteries, dead or alive.

---

**(TO)** increase the balance beam's sensitivity. To write more complex balance beam equations.

## MATH IN THE BALANCE (2)　　◯　　　　　Balancing (　　)

1. Cut out the Tilt Gauge. Fold the top and bottom forward on the dotted lines.

2. Tape it around half a clothespin so the flaps stick out. Rubber-band this to another can of the same height so the zero mark is even with the can's top rim.

3. Slide a light rubber band somewhere on your meter stick, to make one end balance near zero on your gauge. Brake its motion by pressing the can and gauge lightly against the end.

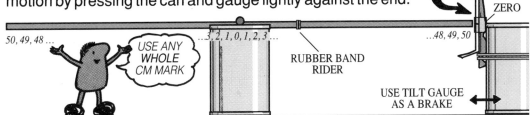

*50, 49, 48 ...*

USE ANY WHOLE CM MARK

*...3, 2, 1, 0, 1, 2, 3 ...*

*...48, 49, 50*

ZERO

RUBBER BAND RIDER

USE TILT GAUGE AS A BRAKE

4. Get 7 coins of equal mass. Return the beam near its zero balance with these combinations of coins at any *whole cm* position. Write an equation:
   a. 1 at 48 cm from the pivot against *6 at one place.*
   b. 1 at 48 cm from the pivot against *triplets in 2 places.*
   c. 1 at 48 cm from the pivot against *pairs in 3 places.*
   d. 1 at 48 cm from the pivot against *6 in different places.*

9

## Answers / Notes

2. *Place the back of the Tilt Gauge against the flat side of the clothespin half, so the top fold is even with the narrow end. Secure with one strip of clear tape around the middle. The width of the gauge wraps around the sides of the wood. This strengthens the projecting flaps, which limit the swing of the beam.*

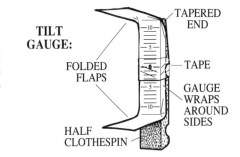

**TILT GAUGE:**

TAPERED END

FOLDED FLAPS

TAPE

GAUGE WRAPS AROUND SIDES

HALF CLOTHESPIN

3. *Demonstrate these braking techniques to your entire class:*
   • *Touch the gauge lightly to the beam as it swings past zero.*
   • *Move it away slightly, allowing minor fluctuations to dampen naturally.*
   • *To speed operations, load the beam while it is still braked near zero, then release.*
   • *It's unnecessary to center the beam exactly at zero, as long as you remember its starting position. If the beam balances at 5 above zero, for example, a correct combination of pennies will return it near 5 above zero again.*

   *With this gauge, students can now place coins at any whole centimeter position, from 1 to 50 on either side, and easily observe a subtle tilt response. Previously, only the 10 cm positions were used.*

4. *Only solution 4a is unique. Many possible solutions fit 4b, 4c and 4d. Where numbers are multiplied, the first represents the number of coins, the second is the distance from the pivot.*

4a. $48 = 6 \times 8$　　　　　4c. $48 = 2 \times 4 + 2 \times 8 + 2 \times 12$

4b. $48 = 3 \times 6 + 3 \times 10$　　4d. $48 = 3 + 5 + 7 + 9 + 11 + 13$

## Materials

☐ The Tilt Gauge. Photocopy this from the supplementary page at the back of the book.
☐ Scissors.
☐ Half of a clothespin. Pull apart a whole one as necessary.
☐ Clear tape.

☐ Two rubber bands.
☐ The meter stick balance previously constructed. The batteries are no longer needed.
☐ A can of equal size to the two that support your meter stick balance.
☐ Seven post-1982 U.S. pennies or other coins of equal mass. If U.S. pennies, check each mint date.

**(TO)** develop a mass standard based on a 10 ml volume of water.

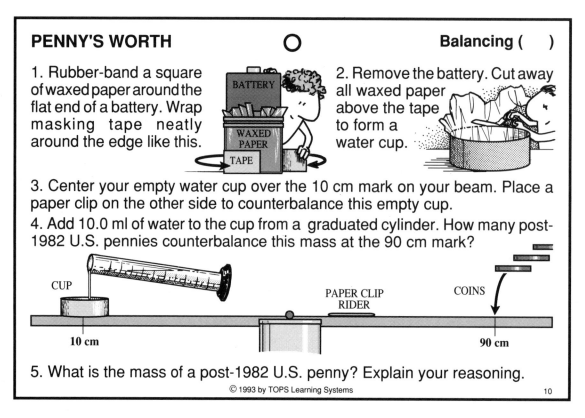

**PENNY'S WORTH** O **Balancing ( )**

1. Rubber-band a square of waxed paper around the flat end of a battery. Wrap masking tape neatly around the edge like this.

2. Remove the battery. Cut away all waxed paper above the tape to form a water cup.

3. Center your empty water cup over the 10 cm mark on your beam. Place a paper clip on the other side to counterbalance this empty cup.

4. Add 10.0 ml of water to the cup from a graduated cylinder. How many post-1982 U.S. pennies counterbalance this mass at the 90 cm mark?

5. What is the mass of a post-1982 U.S. penny? Explain your reasoning.

© 1993 by TOPS Learning Systems                                           10

## Answers / Notes

4. Four pennies counterbalance 10.0 ml of water.

5. Since water has a density of 1 g/ml, 10.0 ml of water has a mass of 10.0 g. This mass is counterbalanced by four post-1982 U.S. pennies of 2.50 g each. (Such a convenient number makes this penny a very fine mass standard!)

## Materials

☐ A rubber band.
☐ Waxed paper.
☐ Scissors.
☐ A size-D battery, dead or alive.
☐ Masking tape.
☐ The meter stick balance with tilt gauge from the previous activity.
☐ A paper clip.
☐ A 10 ml graduated cylinder.
☐ Water.
☐ Four post-1982 U.S. pennies. If these are not available, substitute other coins of uniform size. If you do, paste in these modifications on steps 4 and 5 before duplicating the task cards.

> 4. Use a graduated cylinder to add 10.0 ml of water to the cup. Add a stack of four or more coins somewhere on the right side to recenter the beam.
>
> 5. Calculate the mass of 1 coin. Show your math.

**(TO)** use balance beam math to calculate the mass of unknown coins, based on the mass of known coins.

---

**SMALL CHANGE** ◯ **Balancing ( )**

1. Center your balance beam near zero. Center a post-1982 U.S. penny precisely over the 10 cm mark.

 a. Counterbalance this penny with a *nickel* somewhere on the other side. Calculate its mass.

 b. Counterbalance this penny with a *dime* somewhere on the other side. Calculate its mass.

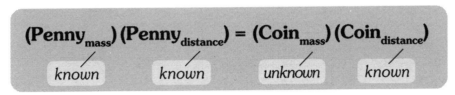

$$(\text{Penny}_{mass})\,(\text{Penny}_{distance}) = (\text{Coin}_{mass})\,(\text{Coin}_{distance})$$
*known*  *known*  *unknown*  *known*

2. Confirm that you accurately calculated the masses of both coins. Substitute your values from step 1 into this equation:

$$(\text{Nickel}_{mass})\,(\text{Nickel}_{distance}) \overset{?}{=} (\text{Dime}_{mass})\,(\text{Dime}_{distance})$$

11

---

## Answers / Notes

1. *The coins need not be centered within the width of the ruler. In fact it is easier to move coins, and read distances, if they hang a little over the near edge.*

*If your students don't know how to solve for the unknown in a simple algebraic equation, now is a good time to teach them. Otherwise consider these options:*

• *Isolate the unknown on your blackboard and ask students to substitute values.*

$$\text{Coin}_{mass} = \text{Penny}_{mass} \times \frac{\text{Penny}_{distance}}{\text{Coin}_{distance}}$$

• *Multiply the mass of the penny (2.5 g) by the correct ratio of pivot distances. If the coin is heavier than the penny, this ratio must be greater than one; If the coin is lighter, it must be less than one.*

1a. *This sample answer for the nickel uses algebra:*
 The penny located 40 cm from the pivot balances a nickel that is 19.6 cm from the pivot.

 $$2.50 \text{ g} \times 40.0 \text{ cm} = \text{Nickel}_{mass} \times 19.6 \text{ cm}$$
 $$\text{Nickel}_{mass} = 2.50 \text{ g} \times 40.0 \text{ cm} / 19.6 \text{ cm} = 5.10 \text{ g}.$$

1b. *This sample answer for the dime uses ratios:*
 The penny located 40 cm from the pivot balances a dime that is 44.1 cm from the pivot. Since the dime is lighter than the penny, we must multiple by a ratio of distances that is less than 1 (40.0/44.1) not greater than 1 (44.1/40.0).

 $$\text{Dime}_{mass} = 2.50 \text{ g} \times 40.0 \text{ cm} / 44.1 \text{ cm} = 2.27 \text{ g}.$$

2.  $$5.10 \text{ g} \times 19.6 \text{ cm} \overset{?}{=} 2.27 \text{ g} \times 44.1 \text{ cm}$$
 $$99.96 \approx 100.11$$

## Materials

☐ The meter stick balance with tilt gauge.
☐ A post-1982 U.S. penny or other mass standard developed in the previous activity.
☐ A nickel and a dime.
☐ A calculator.

---

**(TO)** construct a mobile and examine the mathematics of its design.

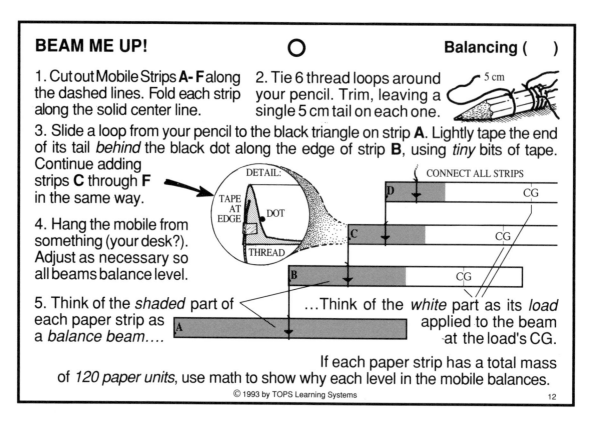

## BEAM ME UP! ○ Balancing ( )

1. Cut out Mobile Strips **A-F** along the dashed lines. Fold each strip along the solid center line.

2. Tie 6 thread loops around your pencil. Trim, leaving a single 5 cm tail on each one.

3. Slide a loop from your pencil to the black triangle on strip **A**. Lightly tape the end of its tail *behind* the black dot along the edge of strip **B**, using *tiny* bits of tape. Continue adding strips **C** through **F** in the same way.

DETAIL:
TAPE AT EDGE
DOT
THREAD

CONNECT ALL STRIPS

D CG
C CG
B CG

4. Hang the mobile from something (your desk?). Adjust as necessary so all beams balance level.

5. Think of the *shaded* part of each paper strip as a *balance beam*....

A

...Think of the *white* part as its *load* applied to the beam at the load's CG.

If each paper strip has a total mass of *120 paper units*, use math to show why each level in the mobile balances.

© 1993 by TOPS Learning Systems

12

## Answers / Notes

*2. Begin with ample thread; it is easier to tie. Push each piece out of the way toward the eraser after it is tied and trimmed. If tangling becomes a problem, each loop can be removed from the pencil after it is constructed.*

*3. For the mathematics of this mobile to work out correctly, each thread must be taped at the very end of the next higher strip. Place the thread and tape between the folded layers, behind the dot.*

   *The thread and tape are assumed to be of negligible mass. For this reason, keep the threads short and the tape pieces as small as possible.*

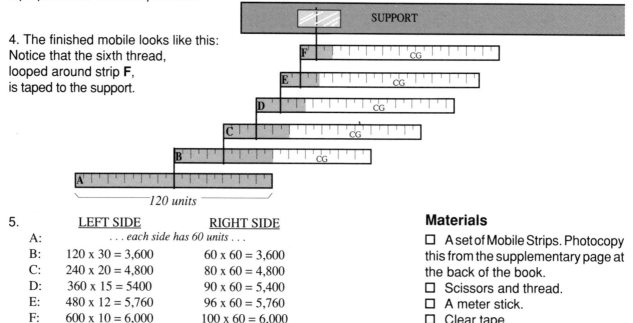

4. The finished mobile looks like this: Notice that the sixth thread, looped around strip **F**, is taped to the support.

SUPPORT
F CG
E CG
D CG
C CG
B CG
A

120 units

5.

| | LEFT SIDE | RIGHT SIDE |
|---|---|---|
| A: | . . . each side has 60 units . . . | |
| B: | 120 x 30 = 3,600 | 60 x 60 = 3,600 |
| C: | 240 x 20 = 4,800 | 80 x 60 = 4,800 |
| D: | 360 x 15 = 5400 | 90 x 60 = 5,400 |
| E: | 480 x 12 = 5,760 | 96 x 60 = 5,760 |
| F: | 600 x 10 = 6,000 | 100 x 60 = 6,000 |

## Materials

☐ A set of Mobile Strips. Photocopy this from the supplementary page at the back of the book.

☐ Scissors and thread.

☐ A meter stick.

☐ Clear tape.

**(TO)** experimentally determine the mass of the meter stick balance beam.

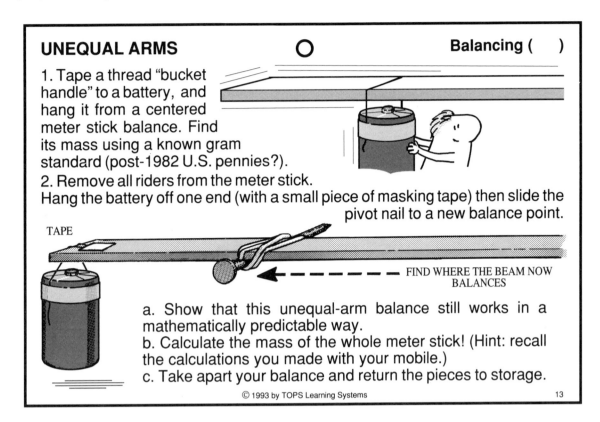

**UNEQUAL ARMS**      O            **Balancing (   )**

1. Tape a thread "bucket handle" to a battery, and hang it from a centered meter stick balance. Find its mass using a known gram standard (post-1982 U.S. pennies?).
2. Remove all riders from the meter stick. Hang the battery off one end (with a small piece of masking tape) then slide the pivot nail to a new balance point.

TAPE

FIND WHERE THE BEAM NOW BALANCES

a. Show that this unequal-arm balance still works in a mathematically predictable way.
b. Calculate the mass of the whole meter stick! (Hint: recall the calculations you made with your mobile.)
c. Take apart your balance and return the pieces to storage.

© 1993 by TOPS Learning Systems        13

## Answers / Notes

1. Sample calculation:
   A 10.0 gram stack of four pennies at a pivot distance of 48.0 cm balanced the battery at a pivot distance of 3.43 cm:

   10.0 g x 48.0 cm = mass of battery x 3.43 cm
   mass of battery = 10.0 g x 48.0/3.43 = 140 g

2a. *Students should add pennies to the unequal-arm balance, demonstrating that this basic relationship still holds true:*   (mass x pivot distance)$_{left}$ = (mass x pivot distance)$_{right}$

2b. Sample calculation:
   The meter stick balances at 25.3 cm. As with the mobile constructed previously, imagine an equal-arm balance centered at this point. The remainder of the meter stick is a load, bearing down at its CG to counterbalance the battery.

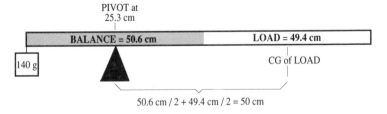

PIVOT at 25.3 cm

BALANCE = 50.6 cm    LOAD = 49.4 cm

140 g              CG of LOAD

50.6 cm / 2 + 49.4 cm / 2 = 50 cm

140 g x 25.3 cm = meter stick load x 50.0 cm

meter stick load = 140 g x 25.3 / 50.0 = 70.8 g

meter stick mass per cm = 70.8 g / 49.4 cm
= 1.43 g/cm

full meter stick = 100 cm x 1.43 g/cm = 143 g

## Materials

☐ Thread.
☐ Masking tape.
☐ A size-D battery or similar dead weight. Our calculations are based on an alkaline battery with a mass of 140 grams. Other types or brands may have less mass, possibly yielding a less dramatic (more nearly equal) unequal-arm balance.

☐ The meter stick balance with tilt gauge.
☐ Post-1982 U.S. pennies or other gram standard. Our calculations are based on a stack of 4 pennies with a mass of 10.0 grams.
☐ A calculator.

**(TO)** cantilever beams beyond the edge of a support. To construct a mathematical series.

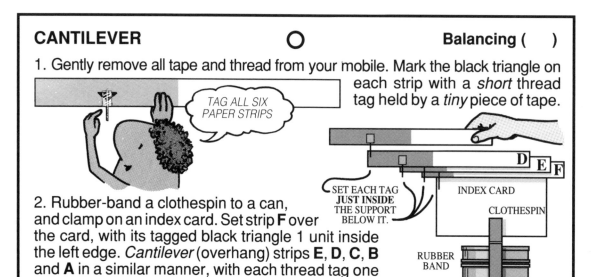

## CANTILEVER ⭕ Balancing ( )

1. Gently remove all tape and thread from your mobile. Mark the black triangle on each strip with a *short* thread tag held by a *tiny* piece of tape.

*TAG ALL SIX PAPER STRIPS*

SET EACH TAG **JUST INSIDE** THE SUPPORT BELOW IT.

INDEX CARD

CLOTHESPIN

RUBBER BAND

2. Rubber-band a clothespin to a can, and clamp on an index card. Set strip **F** over the card, with its tagged black triangle 1 unit inside the left edge. *Cantilever* (overhang) strips **E**, **D**, **C**, **B** and **A** in a similar manner, with each thread tag one unit inside the edge beneath.

    a. How many total units does the cantilever extend to the left of the index card?

    b. Why doesn't the cantilever fall off the edge of the card?

    c. If the thread and tape were not adding extra weight, you could theoretically cantilever 1/2 A + 1/4 B + ... (finish the series).

    d. Calculate the maximum theoretical overhang for 6 beams. Show your math.

14

## Introduction

Get a stack of uniform textbooks or a deck of cards. Introduce the notion of cantilevers by trying to support the top book or card fully beyond the edge of the table.

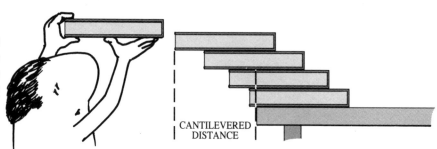

CANTILEVERED DISTANCE

## Answers / Notes

2a. The beams cantilever one full beam plus about 21 units more: 120 units + 21 units = 141 units.

2b. The cantilever doesn't fall off because the CG for all of the beams together remains just inside the edge of the supporting card.

2c. 1/2 A + 1/4 B + 1/6 C + 1/8 D + 1/10 E + 1/12 F. *(The black triangle on each strip determines these fractions.)*

2d. *Students should add up this series — a great exercise with fractions! Since all the beams have equal length, the letters may be dropped.*

    Maximum extension = 1/2 + 1/4 + 1/6 + 1/8 + 1/10 + 1/12

                       = 60/120 + 30/120 + 20/120 + 15/120 + 12/120 + 10/120

                       = 147/120 = 120/120 + 27/120 = 1.225 beam lengths, or 147 units.

## Extension

How many strips will theoretically cantilever to 1 full length? To 2 full lengths?

    *Convert each term in the series* 1/2 + 1/4 + 1/6 +... *to 7 decimal places:* .5000000 + .2500000 + .1666666 +.... *Add them on a printing calculator until their sum exceeds one (4 terms), then two (31 terms).*

## Materials

☐ The folded strips recycled from the mobile in activity 12.

☐ Thread.
☐ Scissors.
☐ Clear tape.
☐ An index card.

☐ A clothespin.
☐ A rubber band.
☐ A can.
☐ A calculator.

**(TO)** calculate the weight of a friend on a balance beam, using your own weight as a standard of comparison.

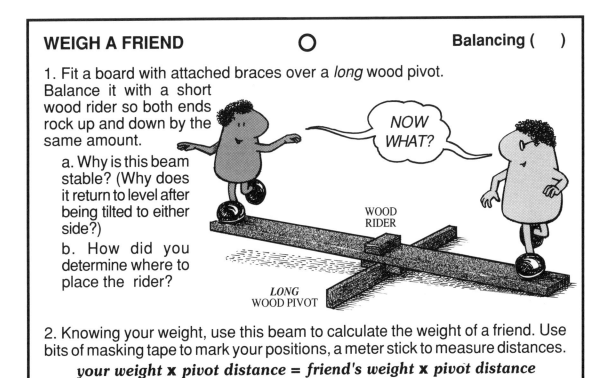

**WEIGH A FRIEND** ○ **Balancing ( )**

1. Fit a board with attached braces over a *long* wood pivot. Balance it with a short wood rider so both ends rock up and down by the same amount.

    a. Why is this beam stable? (Why does it return to level after being tilted to either side?)

    b. How did you determine where to place the rider?

*NOW WHAT?*

WOOD RIDER

*LONG* WOOD PIVOT

2. Knowing your weight, use this beam to calculate the weight of a friend. Use bits of masking tape to mark your positions, a meter stick to measure distances.

*your weight* **x** *pivot distance = friend's weight* **x** *pivot distance*

15

## Answers / Notes

1a. The beam is stable because its CG is centered over the flat bottom of the pivot. Tip the beam in either direction, and it rocks onto an edge of the pivot. This raises the CG, which then falls back to stable equilibrium when the beam is released. *(If the pivot tapered to a thin edge, the beam would not be stable because the CG would fall to a lower position on either side of the pivot.)*

RIDER

1b. When the rider was at the right place, the beam hit the floor with the same impact on both sides and rocked through the same distance.

2. *To prevent possible falls, a "spotter" should stand near each of the students on the beam, ready to offer a steadying hand. Keep feet and hands out from under the beam when it's being used. Prohibit roughhousing — this is fun, but it's not a game!*

    *An easy way to calculate a friend's weight is to multiply your own weight by the ratio of distances. If you are heavier, this ratio is greater than 1. If you are lighter, it is less than 1.*

## Materials

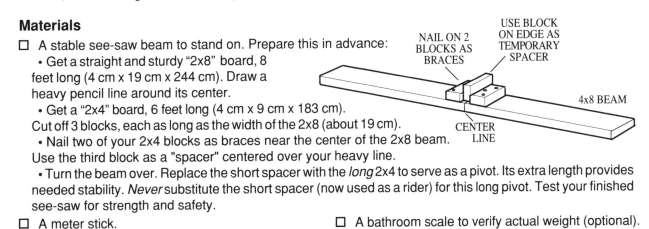

☐ A stable see-saw beam to stand on. Prepare this in advance:

    • Get a straight and sturdy "2x8" board, 8 feet long (4 cm x 19 cm x 244 cm). Draw a heavy pencil line around its center.

    • Get a "2x4" board, 6 feet long (4 cm x 9 cm x 183 cm). Cut off 3 blocks, each as long as the width of the 2x8 (about 19 cm).

    • Nail two of your 2x4 blocks as braces near the center of the 2x8 beam. Use the third block as a "spacer" centered over your heavy line.

    • Turn the beam over. Replace the short spacer with the *long* 2x4 to serve as a pivot. Its extra length provides needed stability. *Never* substitute the short spacer (now used as a rider) for this long pivot. Test your finished see-saw for strength and safety.

☐ A meter stick.

☐ A bathroom scale to verify actual weight (optional).

NAIL ON 2 BLOCKS AS BRACES

USE BLOCK ON EDGE AS TEMPORARY SPACER

4x8 BEAM

CENTER LINE

**(TO)** calculate your mass in kilograms using water jugs and a balance beam.

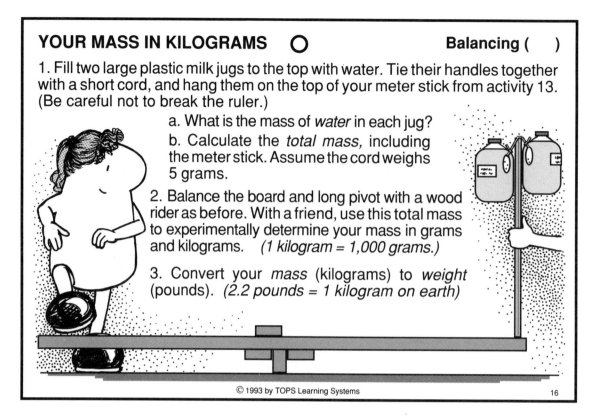

**YOUR MASS IN KILOGRAMS**  ◯                    **Balancing (   )**

1. Fill two large plastic milk jugs to the top with water. Tie their handles together with a short cord, and hang them on the top of your meter stick from activity 13. (Be careful not to break the ruler.)

a. What is the mass of *water* in each jug?

b. Calculate the *total mass,* including the meter stick. Assume the cord weighs 5 grams.

2. Balance the board and long pivot with a wood rider as before. With a friend, use this total mass to experimentally determine your mass in grams and kilograms.    *(1 kilogram = 1,000 grams.)*

3. Convert your *mass* (kilograms) to *weight* (pounds). *(2.2 pounds = 1 kilogram on earth)*

© 1993 by TOPS Learning Systems                    16

## Answers / Notes

1a.  1 gallon x $\dfrac{3.78 \text{ liter}}{\text{gallon}}$ x $\dfrac{1{,}000 \text{ ml}}{\text{liter}}$ x $\dfrac{1 \text{ gram}}{\text{ml}}$ = 3,780 g water

1b.

$$\text{mass of water in 2 jugs} = 3{,}780 \text{ g} \times 2 = 7{,}560 \text{ g}$$
$$\text{mass of 2 jugs} = 70 \text{ g} \times 2 = 140 \text{ g}$$
$$\text{mass of cord} = 5 \text{ g}$$
$$\text{mass of meter stick (from activity 13)} = 142 \text{ g}$$
$$\text{total mass} = 7847 \text{ g}$$

2-3. *Students should calculate their mass based on this relationship:*

$$\text{load} \times \text{pivot distance} = \text{your mass} \times \text{pivot distance}$$

*Here is a sample calculation based on the author's mass:*

$$\text{water jug mass} = 7847 \text{ g}$$
$$\text{load's pivot distance} = 118.9 \text{ cm}$$
$$\text{author's pivot distance} = 11.7 \text{ cm}$$
$$\text{author's mass} = 7{,}847 \text{ g} \times \dfrac{118.9 \text{ cm}}{11.7 \text{ cm}} = 79{,}744 \text{ g} \approx 80 \text{ kg}$$
$$80 \text{ kg} \times 2.2 \text{ pounds/kg} = 176 \text{ pounds}$$

## Extension

British and American measurement commonly tells us the *weight* of an object, rather than its *mass*. What's the difference? Write a report.

## Materials

☐  Two large plastic milk cartons, with handles and lids, of known mass. Weigh these in advance, and label their mass plus holding capacity on each carton like this:

*mass of container = 70 grams*
*capacity = 1 gallon = 3.78 liters*

☐  A short segment (30 cm) of cord.
☐  Water.
☐  A meter stick of known mass. Use the one from activity 13.
☐  The large see-saw balance beam with a wood block rider from the previous activity.

# REPRODUCIBLE
# STUDENT
# TASK CARDS

# Task Cards Options

### Here are 3 management options to consider before you photocopy:

**1. Consumable Worksheets:** Copy 1 complete set of task card pages. Cut out each card and fix it to a separate sheet of boldly lined paper. Duplicate a class set of each worksheet master you have made, 1 per student. Direct students to follow the task card instructions at the top of each page, then respond to questions in the lined space underneath.

**2. Nonconsumable Reference Booklets:** Copy and collate the 2-up task card pages in sequence. Make perhaps half as many sets as the students who will use them. Staple each set in the upper left corner, both front and back to prevent the outside pages from working loose. Tell students that these task card booklets are for reference only. They should use them as they would any textbook, responding to questions on their own papers, returning them unmarked and in good shape at the end of the module.

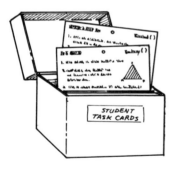

**3. Nonconsumable Task Cards:** Copy several sets of task card pages. Laminate them, if you wish, for extra durability, then cut out each card to display in your room. You might pin cards to bulletin boards; or punch out the holes and hang them from wall hooks (you can fashion hooks from paper clips and tape these to the wall); or fix cards to cereal boxes with paper fasteners, 4 to a box; or keep cards on designated reference tables. The important thing is to provide enough task card reference points about your classroom to avoid a jam of too many students at any one location. Two or 3 task card sets should accommodate everyone, since different students will use different cards at different times.

## CENTER OF GRAVITY   Balancing (    )

1. On an index card, draw diagonal lines that touch each corner. Use a can to give the card a curve, keeping its diagonals to the inside.

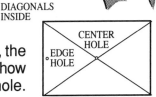

2. Lightly rest your card on a pinpoint where the diagonals cross. Rotate it *horizontally*.

  a. This balance point is called the *center of gravity* (CG). Where is the CG on your index card?

  b. Poke two pinholes through this card: one at its CG, the other near any edge away from the corners. Compare how the card spins *vertically* around a pin through each hole.

3. Tape a penny to a corner of your card. Spin the card on a pin point to locate its new CG, then make a pinhole at this point.

  a. Label this new CG. Compare spinning motions around this point with the other two holes.

  b. Is the CG still centered in the middle of the card? In the middle of its total mass? Explain.

(Write your name on the card and save it.)

1

---

## PLUMB LINE   Balancing (    )

1. Tie a loop at one end of about 20 cm of thread. Tie a paper clip at the other end, and trim.

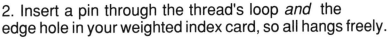

2. Insert a pin through the thread's loop *and* the edge hole in your weighted index card, so all hangs freely.

  a. Where is the CG in relation to the thread?

  b. Now hang everything from the center hole. Does the plumb line still cross the CG?

  c. Poke a 4th hole in the card, away from the others. Does the plumb line still cross the CG from this new hole?

3. Cut a 6 cm square from the corner of a *new* index card.

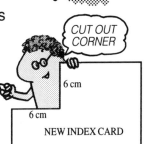

  a. Use your plumb line to experimentally locate and label the card's CG. Explain how you did this.

  b. Confirm that its CG is accurately placed. Explain how you did this.

(Write your name on this card and save it for the next activity.)

2

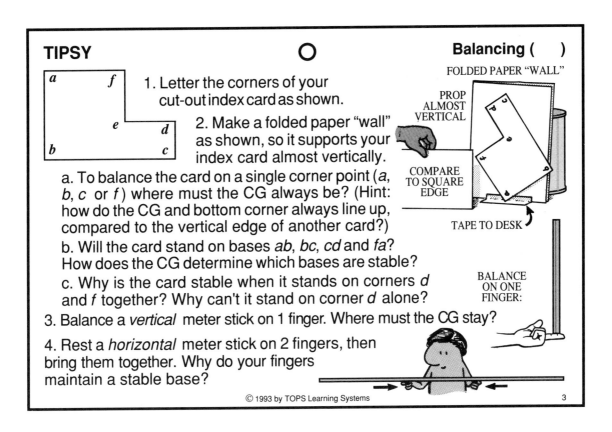

## TIPSY ○ Balancing ( )

FOLDED PAPER "WALL"

1. Letter the corners of your cut-out index card as shown.

2. Make a folded paper "wall" as shown, so it supports your index card almost vertically.

PROP ALMOST VERTICAL

COMPARE TO SQUARE EDGE

TAPE TO DESK

a. To balance the card on a single corner point (*a*, *b*, *c* or *f*) where must the CG always be? (Hint: how do the CG and bottom corner always line up, compared to the vertical edge of another card?)

b. Will the card stand on bases *ab*, *bc*, *cd* and *fa*? How does the CG determine which bases are stable?

c. Why is the card stable when it stands on corners *d* and *f* together? Why can't it stand on corner *d* alone?

BALANCE ON ONE FINGER:

3. Balance a *vertical* meter stick on 1 finger. Where must the CG stay?

4. Rest a *horizontal* meter stick on 2 fingers, then bring them together. Why do your fingers maintain a stable base?

© 1993 by TOPS Learning Systems    3

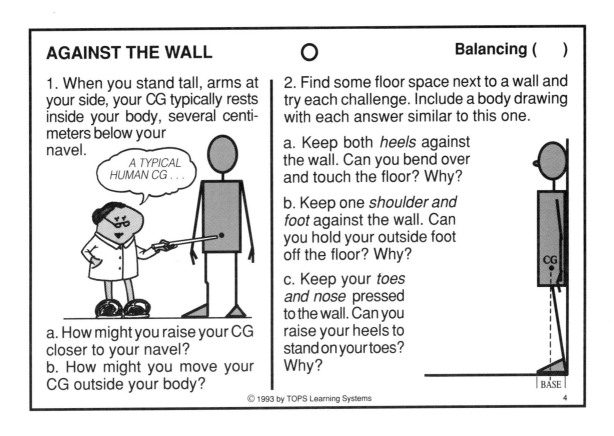

## AGAINST THE WALL ○ Balancing ( )

1. When you stand tall, arms at your side, your CG typically rests inside your body, several centimeters below your navel.

*A TYPICAL HUMAN CG . . .*

a. How might you raise your CG closer to your navel?
b. How might you move your CG outside your body?

2. Find some floor space next to a wall and try each challenge. Include a body drawing with each answer similar to this one.

a. Keep both *heels* against the wall. Can you bend over and touch the floor? Why?

b. Keep one *shoulder and foot* against the wall. Can you hold your outside foot off the floor? Why?

c. Keep your *toes and nose* pressed to the wall. Can you raise your heels to stand on your toes? Why?

CG

BASE

© 1993 by TOPS Learning Systems    4

## STABLE / UNSTABLE / NEUTRAL ○      Balancing ( )

1. Get 2 cans with both ends removed. Use a wad of newspaper to wedge a size-D battery inside one of them. Mark the CG of each system as shown:

Draw an "x" on tape. The CG is located inside the battery behind this x. ➡

 Tape 2 threads across the end of a can to form an "x." The CG is in the center of the can behind this x. ➡

2. Roll both cans across the floor.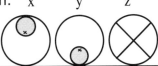
   a. Describe how they move and stop.
   b. Sketch how the CG moves in each rolling can relative to the floor.

3. Balance the cans in each position **x**, **y** and **z** as shown:   x     y     z
   a. Which position is stable? Unstable? Neutral?
   b. When you move the can at each position, does its CG rise or fall?

4. The *equilibrium* of a balanced object describes its stability.
   a. Draw a battery in 3 equilibrium positions — stable, unstable and neutral.
   b. When you push it off each equilibrium, how does its CG shift?

   5

---

## DANCING ON A PINHEAD ○      Balancing ( )

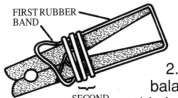
FIRST RUBBER BAND

SECOND RUBBER BAND

1. Hold a thin rubber band over the open end of a clothespin. Secure it with another rubber band near the spring.

2. Clamp the clothespin on the rim of a can, then try to balance a straw on the rubber band. Is its equilibrium stable in this position? Use a drawing to explain why.

3. Hang a clothespin on each end of the straw. How does this affect its equilibrium? Use a drawing to explain your observations.

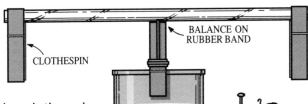
BALANCE ON RUBBER BAND
CLOTHESPIN

4. Take both rubber bands off the clothespin. Use them to strap a clothespin "wing" to the side of the can.
   a. Clamp a pin, head up, in the clothespin.
   b. Try this challenge: fix as many paper clips as you like to a *second* pin, so it "toe-dances" on the head of the first!
   c. Sketch your design. Explain why it has stable equilibrium.

   6

## METER STICK BALANCE    Balancing (   )

1. Rubber-band a nail directly over the 50 cm mark of a meter stick. Wind the rubber band *tightly* over both ends of the nail.

2. Rest the meter stick (nail side up) between 2 cans. Tape a paper clip somewhere underneath so the beam rests level.

RUBBER BAND

BOTTOM DETAIL:

RUBBER BAND

PAPER CLIP RIDER TO LEVEL

3. The beam now balances with the nail on top. Will it also balance with the nail underneath? Why?

4. Use your balance to compare the masses of different coins. If possible include a U.S. penny minted before 1982, and another minted after 1982.

   a. Order the coins from lightest to heaviest. Explain how you did this.

   b. Write your initials on the masking tape that holds the paper clip to your meter stick. Save it to use in activities that follow.

© 1993 by TOPS Learning Systems     7

---

## MATH IN THE BALANCE (1)    Balancing (   )

1. Balance your meter stick between cans as before. Set a battery under each end so the beam can't tilt too far.

2. Get 3 coins of equal mass. Balance them on the beam at the 10 cm positions shown in 2a:

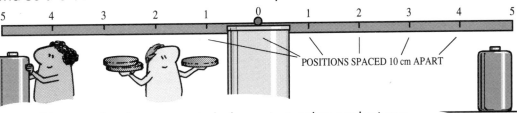

POSITIONS SPACED 10 cm APART

   a. Diagram 3 unique ways to balance two coins against one.

   b. When does the beam balance? Develop a rule.

3. Get 6 coins of equal mass.

   a. Diagram how the beam looks expressing this equation:  2x2 + 5 = 3x3.

   b. Invent 3 more interesting equations that use all 6 coins.

   c. Restate your rule for a balanced beam in terms of the *number* of coins at each position and their *distance* from the pivot.

© 1993 by TOPS Learning Systems     8

## MATH IN THE BALANCE (2)  ◯                    Balancing ( )

1. Cut out the Tilt Gauge. Fold the top and bottom forward on the dotted lines.

2. Tape it around half a clothespin so the flaps stick out. Rubber-band this to another can of the same height so the zero mark is even with the can's top rim.

3. Slide a light rubber band somewhere on your meter stick, to make one end balance near zero on your gauge. Brake its motion by pressing the can and gauge lightly against the end.

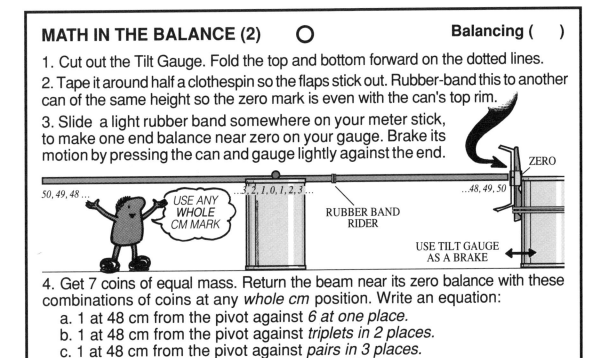

4. Get 7 coins of equal mass. Return the beam near its zero balance with these combinations of coins at any *whole cm* position. Write an equation:
   a. 1 at 48 cm from the pivot against *6 at one place.*
   b. 1 at 48 cm from the pivot against *triplets in 2 places.*
   c. 1 at 48 cm from the pivot against *pairs in 3 places.*
   d. 1 at 48 cm from the pivot against *6 in different places.*

9

---

## PENNY'S WORTH  ◯                    Balancing ( )

1. Rubber-band a square of waxed paper around the flat end of a battery. Wrap masking tape neatly around the edge like this.

2. Remove the battery. Cut away all waxed paper above the tape to form a water cup.

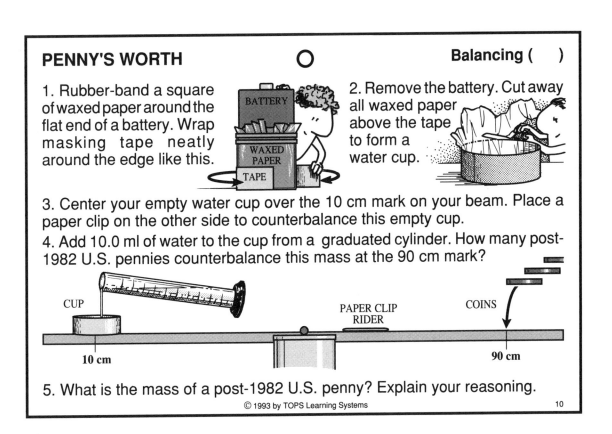

3. Center your empty water cup over the 10 cm mark on your beam. Place a paper clip on the other side to counterbalance this empty cup.

4. Add 10.0 ml of water to the cup from a graduated cylinder. How many post-1982 U.S. pennies counterbalance this mass at the 90 cm mark?

5. What is the mass of a post-1982 U.S. penny? Explain your reasoning.

10

## SMALL CHANGE  Balancing (   )

1. Center your balance beam near zero. Center a post-1982 U.S. penny precisely over the 10 cm mark.

    a. Counterbalance this penny with a *nickel* somewhere on the other side. Calculate its mass.

    b. Counterbalance this penny with a *dime* somewhere on the other side. Calculate its mass.

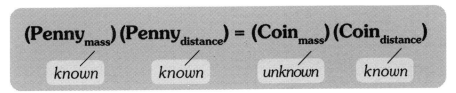

$$(\text{Penny}_{\text{mass}})\ (\text{Penny}_{\text{distance}}) = (\text{Coin}_{\text{mass}})\ (\text{Coin}_{\text{distance}})$$

    *known*      *known*      *unknown*      *known*

2. Confirm that you accurately calculated the masses of both coins. Substitute your values from step 1 into this equation:

$$(\text{Nickel}_{\text{mass}})\ (\text{Nickel}_{\text{distance}}) \stackrel{?}{=} (\text{Dime}_{\text{mass}})\ (\text{Dime}_{\text{distance}})$$

11

---

## BEAM ME UP!  Balancing (   )

1. Cut out Mobile Strips **A-F** along the dashed lines. Fold each strip along the solid center line.

2. Tie 6 thread loops around your pencil. Trim, leaving a single 5 cm tail on each one.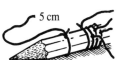

3. Slide a loop from your pencil to the black triangle on strip **A**. Lightly tape the end of its tail *behind* the black dot along the edge of strip **B**, using *tiny* bits of tape.

Continue adding strips **C** through **F** in the same way.

DETAIL:
TAPE AT EDGE
DOT
THREAD

CONNECT ALL STRIPS
D    CG
C    CG
B    CG

4. Hang the mobile from something (your desk?). Adjust as necessary so all beams balance level.

5. Think of the *shaded* part of each paper strip as a *balance beam*....
A

...Think of the *white* part as its *load* applied to the beam at the load's CG.

If each paper strip has a total mass of *120 paper units*, use math to show why each level in the mobile balances.

12

---

## UNEQUAL ARMS  O  Balancing (   )

1. Tape a thread "bucket handle" to a battery, and hang it from a centered meter stick balance. Find its mass using a known gram standard (post-1982 U.S. pennies?).
2. Remove all riders from the meter stick. Hang the battery off one end (with a small piece of masking tape) then slide the pivot nail to a new balance point.

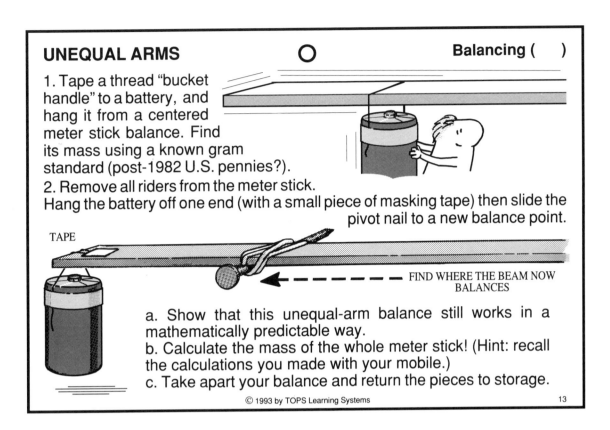

TAPE

FIND WHERE THE BEAM NOW BALANCES

a. Show that this unequal-arm balance still works in a mathematically predictable way.
b. Calculate the mass of the whole meter stick! (Hint: recall the calculations you made with your mobile.)
c. Take apart your balance and return the pieces to storage.

13

## CANTILEVER  O  Balancing (   )

1. Gently remove all tape and thread from your mobile. Mark the black triangle on each strip with a *short* thread tag held by a *tiny* piece of tape.

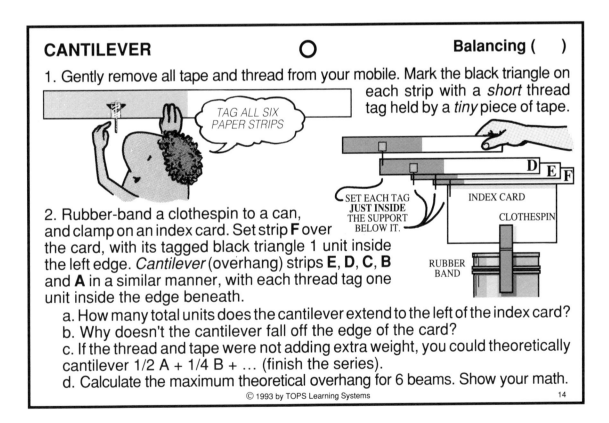

TAG ALL SIX PAPER STRIPS

SET EACH TAG **JUST INSIDE** THE SUPPORT BELOW IT.

**D** **E** **F**

INDEX CARD

CLOTHESPIN

RUBBER BAND

2. Rubber-band a clothespin to a can, and clamp on an index card. Set strip **F** over the card, with its tagged black triangle 1 unit inside the left edge. *Cantilever* (overhang) strips **E**, **D**, **C**, **B** and **A** in a similar manner, with each thread tag one unit inside the edge beneath.

a. How many total units does the cantilever extend to the left of the index card?
b. Why doesn't the cantilever fall off the edge of the card?
c. If the thread and tape were not adding extra weight, you could theoretically cantilever 1/2 A + 1/4 B + ... (finish the series).
d. Calculate the maximum theoretical overhang for 6 beams. Show your math.

14

## WEIGH A FRIEND  ○         Balancing (  )

1. Fit a board with attached braces over a *long* wood pivot. Balance it with a short wood rider so both ends rock up and down by the same amount.

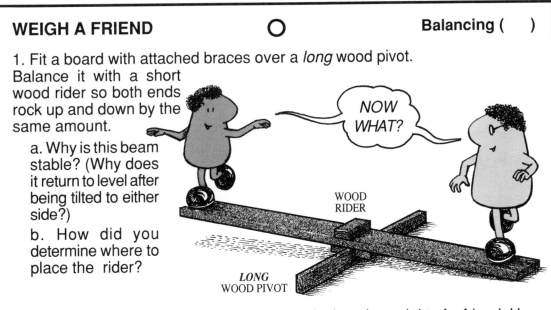

   a. Why is this beam stable? (Why does it return to level after being tilted to either side?)

   b. How did you determine where to place the rider?

2. Knowing your weight, use this beam to calculate the weight of a friend. Use bits of masking tape to mark your positions, a meter stick to measure distances.

**your weight x pivot distance = friend's weight x pivot distance**

15

---

## YOUR MASS IN KILOGRAMS  ○         Balancing (  )

1. Fill two large plastic milk jugs to the top with water. Tie their handles together with a short cord, and hang them on the top of your meter stick from activity 13. (Be careful not to break the ruler.)

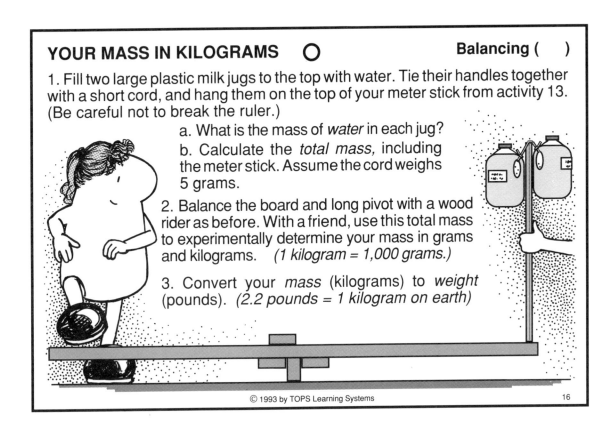

   a. What is the mass of *water* in each jug?

   b. Calculate the *total mass,* including the meter stick. Assume the cord weighs 5 grams.

2. Balance the board and long pivot with a wood rider as before. With a friend, use this total mass to experimentally determine your mass in grams and kilograms. *(1 kilogram = 1,000 grams.)*

3. Convert your *mass* (kilograms) to *weight* (pounds). *(2.2 pounds = 1 kilogram on earth)*

16

# SUPPLEMENTARY PAGE

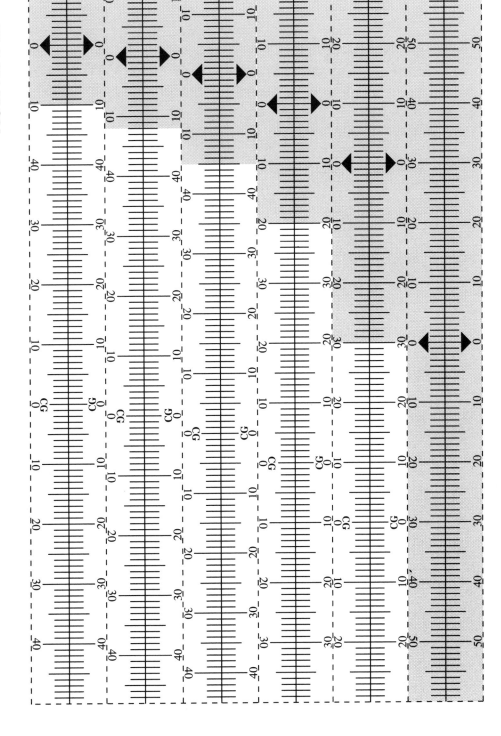

**MOBILE STRIPS**
ACTIVITY 12

**TILT GAUGE**
ACTIVITY 9